seaSide

INTRODUCTION

A day at the seaside! Building sandcastles; all the fun of the fair; crazy golf; windsurfing; messing about in rock pools; splashing about in the surf; some fish and chips; a ride on a tram or a donkey; the excitement of a roller coaster; a stick of rock; soaring sea birds; and lovely wild flowers on the cliffs.

These are just a few of the joys to be had for anyone visiting the coast. And for the older 'seaside-ites' there's always a spot of paddling or simply lying in the sun for a rest.

Since Victorian times, British seaside resorts have attracted tourists throughout the summer months when there's a fair chance of good weather. But even in the winter, when the wind is whipping up the sea into a fury of white spume, the seaside has much to offer, even though the beach huts may be locked and the ice cream vans nowhere to be seen – or heard. Whatever the time of year, there is always something interesting to i-SPY at the seaside.

The next time you go to the seaside, take your i-SPY book with you and keep it handy when you're digging in the sand or walking along the pier. You never know what you might see next.

How to use your i-SPY book

As you work through this book, you will notice that the subjects are arranged in groups which are related to the kinds of places where you are likely to find things. You need 1000 points to send off for your i-SPY certificate (see page 64) but that is not too difficult because there are masses of points in every book. Each entry has a star or circle and points value beside it. The stars represent harder to spot entries. As you make each i-SPY, write your score in the circle or star. There are questions dotted throughout the book that can double your i-SPY score. Check your answers on page 63.

55748

CHILDRENS
GENERAL INTEREST
£2-99.

Points: 10

OPEN-TOP BUS

Many seaside resorts run an open-top bus – a perfect way to see the sights, especially on a sunny day!

CLIFF RAILWAY

Points: 10
double with answer

These short railways run up and down a steep gradient from the bottom to the top of the cliff in some seaside towns. They often save you walking up lots of steps.

What is a funicular railway?

The word 'promenade', often shortened to prom, is taken from the French word 'promener', meaning 'to walk'. Most seaside towns have a paved walkway along the seashore which is traffic free.

PUNCH AND JUDY

Top Spot!   **Points: 25**

Good old-fashioned fun! First seen in Britain in the 17th century, Punch and Judy shows are normally performed by a single 'professor', who controls both the puppets.

Do you know what the name Punch is short for?

BEACH HUTS

Some resorts have long lines of these little cabins. Usually they are quite small with just enough room to change into a swimming costume and to make a cup of tea.

Points: 10

DECK CHAIR

No seaside town would be complete without its deck chairs and their attendants. Many comedy sketches have centred upon the tangles which some people get into when putting them up.

Points: 5

TELESCOPE

You'll often find these telescopes at the seaside. You put a coin in the slot and the telescope works until your time runs out.

Points: 5

SEASIDE SHELTER

You can enjoy the sea air in the worst of weather by sitting in one of these shelters. They are usually positioned so that you can see the sea while being protected from the wind.

Points: 10

PLEASURE PIERS

Many seaside resorts have long piers reaching out into the sea.

Points: 10

THEATRE

The traditional theatre on a pier is a good place to see a top act or entertainer.

Points: 15

FUNFAIR

The fun doesn't stop at the prom. Funfairs, at the end of the pier, have been popular since Victorian times.

Points: 10

CANNON

All around the coast you will find coastal defences from different periods of British history. Sometimes cannons have been recovered from old ships and set up for decoration.

Points: 20

BLACKPOOL TOWER

Top Spot!　　Points: 25

Blackpool Tower is one of Britain's most famous seaside structures. It was opened in 1894 and took just under three years to build. It was inspired by the the Eiffel Tower in Paris.

Points: 15

GRAND HOTEL

If you're spending a holiday at the seaside, you may be lucky enough to stay in one of the very luxurious hotels that you can find on the seafronts of the bigger and more famous resorts. Today, these hotels are often used for business conferences and many seaside towns have hotels called The Grand.

LIGHTHOUSE

Points: 15

The lights from lighthouses warn sailors of dangers, such as rocks. In the past, most lighthouses were manned by humans who had to make sure everything was in working order and that the lights were lit when necessary. Nowadays, however, they are automatic.

Points: 20

BOARDWALK

Many beaches are reached by a short walk from a car park. These wooden structures make it easy to walk across the sandy paths and are used to stop erosion.

PADDLING DOG

Points: 10

Just like us, dogs enjoy a good splash about in the sea and often they don't seem to mind that the water is cold. Watch out when they get out and shake the water off!

Points: 10

BEACH CLEANING

After you have gone home, the hard work of cleaning up the beach begins, for the next day's activity.

Jason Batterham / Shutterstock.com

8

BEACH TENT

Points: 5

These little tents are a popular way to change into your swimming costume and shelter from the wind and sun.

Points: 5

WINDBREAK

If it's blustery, these portable walls are a really good way to keep the wind off.

BEACHCOMBING

Points: 15

Beachcombing has changed in recent years! Coin collectors, archaeologists, and treasure hunters may be found painstakingly scanning the sand with their metal detectors.

Points: 10

Modern wetsuits enable swimmers and surfers to go into the sea, even when the water is cold.

 Points: 15

Some beaches have a permanent volleyball court – if not you can always make your own.

Multibomi Nikolay / Shutterstock.com

Points: 20

A flat beach, a windy day, a huge kite and a set of wheels. Watch out – landboarders can reach high speeds.

Points: 10

A game of beach cricket is always fun, no bouncers and lots of soft sand for diving catches!

Top Spot! Points: 25

This modern sport takes full advantage of the wind as the large kite pulls the buggy along below. Take care of them on the beach as they travel very fast.

Points: 10

A slower game to be enjoyed by all ages.

CANOE

Take to the sea in a canoe but be careful not to paddle too far out to sea. Always do this with a responsible adult.

Points: 15

WINDSURFING

This popular and active sport uses a flat, buoyant board, similar to a surfboard. It takes considerable skill and practice to balance and manoeuvre.

Points: 15

JET SKI

A speedy but noisy way to get around. Lifeguards also use them to rescue people in difficulty.

Points: 15

KAYAKING

One paddle and away you go! Make sure you have an adult with you when you do this.

Points: 20

SURFER

It takes a lot of practice, but boards are easy to hire these days. You can do this for hours!

Points: 10

SURF SCHOOL

Pawel Burchenko / Shutterstock.com

A really good way to learn how to surf is to enrol in a special school. Best of all is that there's no homework!

Points: 15

BODYBOARD

If you can't manage to stand on a surfboard, bodyboarding is also great fun.

Points: 10

KITESURFER

The adventurous and energetic use the wind to propel themselves across the water.

Points: 30   Top Spot!

PONTOON

Points: 15

A pontoon is like a floating bridge that is anchored to the seabed. Reaching a boat is easy from a fixed pontoon or jetty.

Points: 25   Top Spot!

DIVING PLATFORM

This is quite an unusual sight around the coast of Britain. It is a floating platform, anchored to the seabed out in a bay which is safe for swimming. If you are a good enough swimmer, you can swim out to it and take a rest or use it for diving.

BRIDGE

Top Spot!   Points: 25

You need to be brave and have a head for heights to traverse a bridge over a coastal ravine – especially if the bridge starts to wobble!

Points: 10

Many seaside towns have a zoo that gives you the opportunity to see a huge variety of different animals – not just animals from the seaside.

Points: 15

A nice distraction especially if the weather is not good – why not ride the slides in a modern pool complex?

Points: 20

Why not bring the sea inside? Aquariums are a great way to explore life beneath the waves.

SWAN RIDE

Points: 10

There are lots of fun ways to pass the time at the seaside. Hire one of these special pedalos and ride a swan.

Points: 10

MODEL BOATS

If you can't get on to the open waves, model boats offer the perfect chance to show off your boating skills.

TRAMPOLINE

Points: 10

A fun way to spend an hour or so. You can challenge your friends to a bouncing competition. But be careful – don't bounce too high!

Points: 10

CRAZY GOLF

Practise your putting skills over the ramps and through the hazards of a game of crazy golf. You'll find people playing crazy golf in most seaside towns – sometimes even in the rain!

SWING BOAT

Points: 10

It takes two to really get into the swing of things. Riders have to take turns to pull on the two ropes inside the boat to make them swing backwards and forwards.

MINIATURE RAILWAY

Points: 15

These mini engines offer a lovely way to travel the fun parks.

Points: 10

DONKEY RIDE

A more traditional ride along the beach, especially for younger visitors, is the donkey ride.

GO-KARTING

Points: 10

If you prefer something a little faster, put your foot down.

Points: 10

WINTER FISHING

Even on cold, dull days you can spy hardy anglers with their beach rods trying for the one that got away last time!

FUN FISHING

Points: 10

You don't need a lot of expensive equipment to go fishing.

Points: 15

CATCH

You should have seen the one that got away! Many fishermen put their catch back in the sea. Score double points for spotting a fish being caught.

For all generations, it's always fun to bury someone – especially if it is an adult!

5 **Points: 5**

The first thing you'll want to do, even if the weather is a bit chilly, is to get down on the beach and try your hand with a bucket and spade.

Sand sculptures can be of anything and everything, copy something from nature or make something out of your imagination. Decorate your sand sculpture with items found on the beach. Here is a mermaid with seaweed hair.

Why not build one yourself and get someone to judge whether or not yours is better than the one in the picture.

You don't have to build upward. You can have a lot of fun in the sand with a stick.

What is the biggest picture you can draw?

PARACHUTE DISPLAYS

Points: 20

Keep your eyes on the sky, too, especially during the main holiday season – you may well see individual or team parachute displays.

Points: 15

HOT-AIR BALLOONING

Hot-air ballooning is becoming increasingly popular as a sport and you will often see the brightly-coloured envelopes around our coastlines during clear days, especially in the early morning.

HANG-GLIDER

Points: 15

Hang-gliders jump off high cliffs and can stay in the air for hours.

22

25 Points: 25   Top Spot!   **RED ARROWS**

The Royal Air Force Aerobatic Team, the Red Arrows, flies overhead in close formation with the rear planes releasing coloured vapour trails. At air shows and around the coasts of Britain, this world-famous team performs its airborne aerobatics.

CANDY FLOSS

Points: 5

Yummy candy floss is always a seaside treat. Try and eat it without it sticking to your nose!

Points: 5

FISH AND CHIPS

Fish and chips and other seafood are perhaps the most traditional of meals to eat at the seaside but other kinds of fast foods can be found, too.

ROCK

Points: 5
double with answer

Perhaps the most famous of all seaside sweets is rock. The best known is peppermint, which is pink on the outside and white in the middle, with the name of the seaside town printed on it.

The name of the town is only on the ends of the stick of rock. True or false?

Points: 5

SWEET SHOP

For anyone with a sweet tooth, the shops along the prom offer a huge selection of sweets.

ICE CREAM VAN

Points: 5

After all that bouncing around, any youngster is sure to want an ice cream or an ice lolly. The different companies which run these vans announce their arrival with different jingles ringing out from the speakers which are often on the top of the van.

SHOES

Points: 5

Great for going on the beach and on rocks. Many shoes designed for the beach are made of plastic or rubber and have holes that let seawater drain out easily.

Points: 5

BUCKETS AND SPADES

A must for the long summer days if you're planning on making a sandcastle or burying your friend in the sand.

INFLATABLES

Points: 5

Make sure you have lots of puff to blow these up! There are lots of different types available from seaside stalls these days – from lilos to huge inflatable sharks.

DROP TOWER

This ride has its ups and downs!

⭐ **Points: 15**

DODGEMS

These car rides are great fun. You are supposed to dodge the other cars – not hit them!

⭐ **Points: 15**

HOUSE OF FUN

The House of Fun usually includes a variety of attractions which are designed to make you laugh!

⭐ **Points: 15**

MERRY-GO-ROUND

Demmos HR / Shutterstock.com

Traditional merry-go-rounds were driven by steam engines, and you can sometimes find steam-driven versions at steam fairs.

What other name is given to merry-go-rounds, especially in the United States?

⭐ **Points: 10**
double with answer

CHAIR-O-PLANE

Top Spot! **Points: 25**

25

These have been a favourite for many years. Chairs are suspended from a big top, which rotates. The chairs then fly outwards, like 'planes', when the ride is in motion. They were a thrill ride of their time and they still remain very popular at fairs today. A modern version of the ride allows the whole ride to climb high above ground level with some of the most thrilling lifting the chairs more than 100ft into the sky.

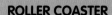

Points: 20

ROLLER COASTER

With its speed and fast turns, the roller coaster is one of the most exciting rides of any funfair but it is especially thrilling by the seaside.

HELTER-SKELTER

Points: 15

The helter-skelter is always a funfair favourite. You slide down from the top of the tower on a special mat. 'Helter-skelter' roughly means 'disorderly haste'. It is thought to have come from an old English word meaning 'to hasten'.

Points: 10

WHEEL TURNER

Not for the faint-hearted!

AMUSEMENT ARCADE

If the weather is bad outside you can cheer yourself up in one of the many amusement arcades.

Points: 10

TOKEN MACHIN

Many attractions do not take cash any more – you will need to exchange your money for a token.

Points: 5

TRY YOUR LUCK

Try your luck at winning a toy by operating the electronic grabber. The more times you try, the more likely you are to win.

Points: 5

BINGO

Who can resist a game of bingo?

Points: 5

Cliffs found along beaches offer the perfect opportunity for rock climbing. Be sure to only try this under supervision and wearing the correct safety equipment like a harness and a helmet.

Points: 20

What could be better than riding a horse along the beach, in and out of the water? You'll find some horse riding schools offer beach excursions with their ponies and horses that can last anything from an hour to a whole day.

Points: 20

For some people beaches are not just sand and sun. These adventurous people are hiking up a steep cliff from the beach. Take care and only do this with adult supervision.

Look out for the various warning and information signs at or near the seaside.

SEA WASH

Points: 10

Take care! The tide can get pretty high in some places.

Points: 5

TOILETS

Toilets are always close at hand at the seaside.

PARKING TICKETS

Points: 5

Be sure to get a parking ticket and pay and display.

Points: 5

NO DOGS

Although most of them love a run on the sand, you are not allowed to take dogs onto some beaches...

DOGS ON LEADS

Points: 10

...whereas on others, you can take them for a walk as long as they are kept on a lead.

Points: 10

CHANGES IN LEVEL

Be careful if you see this sign. The submerged beach may suddenly drop away.

LITTER BIN

Always put your litter in the bins provided.

5 **Points: 5**

ALCOHOL-FREE ZONE

No alcohol should be drunk on beaches with this sign.

Points: 10

CYCLE LANE

Cycling on the prom is always fun – but be sure to look both ways if you cross a cycle path.

10 **Points: 10**

GROYNES

Beach groynes perform a very important role – *what is a groyne?*

Points: 10
double with answer

Points: 15

This is a modern 'ro-ro' (roll-on/roll-off) ferry for carrying cars, trucks, and passengers. It can carry more than 2000 passengers and up to 650 vehicles.

ACHT

Points: 15

Many yachts have no motors and rely on wind power for movement.

Points: 25   Top Spot!

LUXURY YACHT

You will find this luxury craft moored at the marina or cruising the high seas for more extended periods on the water.

OLD SHIPS

Points: 25   Top Spot!

Britain has a long maritime history and there have been many famous sea captains and ships. HMS Victory, Lord Nelson's famous flagship, can be seen in Portsmouth harbour.

SCHOONER

Top Spot!   **Points: 25**

Schooners were mainly used as cargo ships but also favoured by pirates from the 16th to 18th centuries. They are sailing ships with at least two masts (foremast and mainmast) with the mainmast being the taller.

DINGHY SAILING

Points: 15

Another popular water sport, there are many different types of dinghies, for one, two or more people. To keep the boat on an even keel, the crew can be suspended from one side on a trapeze.

CRUISE LINER

You may see a luxury cruise liner departing on an ocean-bound trip. These massive floating hotels can carry thousands of guests.

Points: 20

BOAT BUILDING

Ships have to be constructed in a special 'dry dock' before they can be launched into the sea.

What is the traditional ceremony for launching a new ship?

Points: 10
double with answer

BOAT TRIPS

By the coast, or at the mouths of some rivers around our shores, you will often find kiosks selling tickets for sightseeing boat trips.

Points: 15

FENDER

Sailing ships and luxury yachts have traditional plastic fenders, or bumpers, hanging along the side to prevent damage. Working ships may have old tyres that do the same job!

Points: 5

FISHING TRAWLER

Points: 15

Trawlers can be quite large boats. They fish well out to sea by dragging a strong net along the seabed to catch bottom-feeding fish.

Points: 10

CONTAINER SHIP

Far out at sea, these massive vessels carry huge amounts of cargo around the world. Everything from telephones to cars are securely packed and transported in the containers loaded on these ships. Some are so tall they look like they will topple over!

HOVERCRAFT

Top Spot! Points: 30

These spectacular vessels travel at great speeds and skim over the surface of the water on a cushion of air.

If you don't mind the smell of fish, a walk around a working fish quay can be full of interest and lots of paraphernalia for i-SPYing.

Points: 5

Floating buoys, attached by ropes, mark lanes rather like white lines painted on the floor of a car park and keep the harbour traffic in good order.

Points: 10

Very often, the contents or cargo in a boat will require a crane or hoist to help lift it to the shore.

Points: 5

Wherever ships are to be moored, you will find bollards. The ships' mooring lines, or hawsers, are made fast (tied) to the bollard to stop the boats floating away.

A lobster fisherman can use quite a small boat to distribute his lobster pots at good sites around the coast before returning to collect them – hopefully with the lobsters trapped within.

How does the fisherman know where the pots are left?

Points: 10

Big ships need big cranes or gantries to assist in their loading and unloading.

Points: 10

This is a much smaller type of fishing boat and you will see lots of these around the coast.

Boats, like cars, need regular maintenance. You may see a fishing boat removed from the water getting its hull repainted, or a yacht getting scrubbed clean to remove debris that would otherwise build up over time and reduce its speed in the water.

Points: 5

Take care when walking down these steps. They are normally slippery due to the seawater and seaweed.

Points: 5

The captains of fishing boats plan their days around the tide. At low tide you may see some boats out of water in the harbour.

Points: 5

You are most likely to see fishing nets curled up on a trawler or laid out on the quay side.

When accidents occur at sea, the courageous members of the Royal National Lifeboat Institution are always on hand to help, no matter how great the risk. The RNLI receives no grants from local or national government, but you will find RNLI collection boxes at the seaside, often in the shape of a lifeboat.

Points: 5 — LIFEGUARD

On busy beaches and those popular with surfers, you might see a lifeguard keeping an eye on the water. RNLI lifeguards regularly patrol up to 200 beaches around the UK.

MARINE RESCUE VEHICLE — Points: 15

This 4x4 vehicle in its distinctive dark blue and yellow colour scheme, and with its roof-mounted lights, is driven by members of Her Majesty's Coastguard.

Points: 20 — LIFEBOAT AT SEA

The RNLI will rush to the aid of anyone in need of assistance. Look out for the powerful rescue boats at sea.

LIFEGUARD VEHICLE

Points: 15

Many beaches, especially those good for surfing, have a lifeguard truck stationed on the beach.

Points: 30   **Top Spot!**

LIFEBOAT LAUNCH

Seeing a RNLI boat launch is always something special. A full-size lifeboat is housed in this type of building which has a slipway down to the sea so that the boat can be launched very quickly from the shore when there is an emergency.

LIFE BUOY

Points: 5

A life buoy can be used as a safety aid if a swimmer is in distress. They are brightly coloured so they can be easily seen, and they float. Never play with these – they need to be in place in case they are needed to help save someone's life.

Points: 25   Top Spot!   **HELICOPTER**

Sometimes the RNLI boat needs assistance from the coastguard helicopter. It can reach people in inaccessible places and whisk them to safety or hospital very quickly.

TAKE CARE

Points: 10

Signs like this one warn of the power of the sea. It is easy to become cut off from the rest of the beach by the incoming tide.

Points: 5

SAFE SWIMMING

Look out for these flags – it means that the area is patrolled by lifeguards. You should only swim in the area between these flags – swimming outside of this area could be dangerous.

BEACH SAFETY

Points: 5

These signs offer a combination of safety instructions – be sure to read them!

Around the coast of mainland Britain, but especially around Scotland, there are offshore islands that can be seen from the seaside. Some, such as the Isle of Skye, are big, while others are no more than large rocks.

Points: 20

Points: 15

The area around beaches is worth exploring. You may find a natural cave in the rocks. Take extra care here – the surface may be slippery with sharp rocks and the inside is sure to be dark!

Along many parts of the coast of Britain your first sight of the seaside will be the cliffs inland from the beach.

Where are Britain's famous 'white cliffs'?

Points: 10
double with answer

A sand dune is a hill of sand which builds up behind a sandy beach. Sand is blown from the beach and trapped by plants, such as marram grass.

Points: 10

A sea arch can form where the waves hollow out a cave on either side of a headland. Eventually the two caves meet to make the arch. Then the sea could wear away the landward side of the arch to cut it off from the coast.

BLACK-HEADED GULL

...ess common at the seaside ...han it used to be, this small ...gull forms flocks in winter. Their ...eads are actually dark brown, ...ut only in summer.

Points: 5

FULMAR

Fulmars are becoming increasingly common. Look for them as they soar elegantly on the currents of air along cliffs. In flight, they have very straight-looking wings.

Points: 10

LESSER BLACK-BACKED GULL

This gull is slightly smaller than the herring gull. Notice its bright yellow beak, legs and feet and of course its black back.

Points: 10

HERRING GULL

Apart from black-headed gulls, which are often seen far from the coast, this is probably the gull you are most likely to see at the seaside. Notice that it has paler wings than the black-backed gull as well as pink feet.

Points: 5

OYSTERCATCHER

Oystercatchers are large, noisy birds with large orange-red beaks. They feed on mussels, cockles, worms and small invertebrates.

 Points: 10

TURNSTONE

These are medium-sized wading birds who prefer stony beaches to sand. They get their name from their habit of turning over stones to find their food.

Points: 15

DUNLIN

A small starling-sized wader which forms huge flocks in winter. They swirl together as the tide covers their feeding grounds.

 Points: 10

SHAG

At first glance, the shag looks similar to a cormorant but it is smaller and is rarely seen away from the sea. Look out for them on rocks. In spring, this bird has a crest on its head.

Points: 15

Flowering plants that live by the sea have to be able to tolerate conditions which would kill inland plants. They must be able to stand windy conditions, being soaked in salt-laden spray, and perhaps be able to survive in only a tiny amount of soil in a crevice or in shingle or sand.

Points: 10

This plant is not confined to the coast and can be found in all kinds of grassy places. It flowers throughout the summer and a carpet of these yellow, pea-like flowers on a cliff top is a beautiful sight.

Points: 10

This plant, a member of the carrot family, is grown commercially for its fleshy leaves and stems, which are sold for use in top restaurants.

Points: 5

You will find this tough grass doing a great job by the sea; it builds sand dunes and protects our coasts from erosion.

SEA LAVENDER

Points: 10

Because of its very shallow roots, sea lavender does not need very much soil to grow and can live on narrow cliff ledges.

Points: 15

SEA HOLLY

Found on shingle beaches and on sand dunes, the blue flower heads and spiky leaves make them look more like thistles than holly.

Points: 15

SEA ASTER

The flowers of this plant resemble those of a garden Michaelmas daisy. It grows in similar places to thrift and flowers from July to October.

SEA CAMPION

Points: 15

This is a variety of the well-known bladder campion which grows along roadsides in much of Britain. It flowers throughout the summer.

Points: 10

THRIFT

This is also known as sea pink. It grows in salt marshes and on sea cliffs and its delicate pink flowers can be seen throughout the summer.

BLUE JELLYFISH

Points: 20

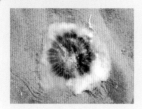

Also known as the bluefire jellyfish, individuals grow to approximately 10–25cm but form into chains made of tens of thousands. They are known to kill fish.

Points: 20

BY-THE-WIND SAILOR

This free-floating sea creature, approximately 7cm in diameter, is easily identified by the small, stiff sail which helps it skim over the oceans to be washed up on our beaches.

SEA URCHIN

Points: 15

A live sea urchin would be a very rare thing to find on the beach. Normally you will only find the hard skeleton (like in the picture), known as a 'test', after a gull has had its meal.

Points: 20

MERMAID'S PURSE

Also called devil's purse, these are the egg cases of the lesser spotted dogfish, or, more unusually, of several species of shark or ray. They will generally be empty as the young fish will have already hatched and left.

PERIWINKLE

Points: 10

The common periwinkle has been collected by humans as food for centuries. They are picked from rocks and rock pools and are often referred to as winkles.

Points: 10

RAZORFISH

This member of the shellfish family is huge! Specimens reach over 20cm long. Fragile, empty shells are often found washed up on the tideline.

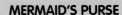

BLENNY

Top Spot! **Points: 25**

Some fish get caught in rock pools when the tide goes out; others, like blennies, live in the pools. If you look under a stone in a rock pool, you may disturb one, but don't forget to replace the stone.

Points: 15

STARFISH

The common starfish has five arms but if in danger, it may deliberately shed one before scuttling away. It can then grow another arm. Starfish feed on shellfish such as mussels.

SEA ANEMONE

Points: 10

Not a flower, but an animal! Look for these beadlet anemones in rock pools. They may be red, green or brown. The 'petals' are actually stinging tentacles which surround the animal's mouth.

Points: 25   Top Spot!

SQUAT LOBSTER

Actually more closely related to crabs, they are much smaller than standard lobsters. They grab food that floats to the bottom of the sea with their sharp front claws.

VELVET CRAB

This is one of our largest crabs. It can swim quite quickly. Its eyes are red and its shell is blue-green in colour but is covered by thin brown fur.

Points: 15

SHORE CRAB

There are more than 50 kinds of crabs living in British waters. This is the common green shore crab which is the one you are most likely to find at the seaside.

Points: 20

HERMIT CRAB

The easiest place to see them is in rock pools. As they grow, they require ever-larger empty shells which they carry on their backs.

Points: 20

EDIBLE CRAB

Mainly nocturnal, the reddish brown adults can reach 25cm and weigh 3kg. They are aggressive if disturbed and will give a serious nip with their very powerful claws. Be careful!

Points: 20

LIMPET

Points: 5

When attacked, these conical molluscs stick to rocks like, well, limpets! This is a survival strategy that has served them well. They can, however, move, and they feed by grazing on nearby algae.

Points: 10

COCKLE

The cockle is a small member of the clam family. At low tide, when it is safe to do so, it can be raked from just underneath the surface of sandy beaches.

RAGWORM

Points: 10

Ragworms are often used by fishermen as they make ideal fishing bait. They are found in muddy or gravelly conditions.

Points: 25   **Top Spot!**

GREY SEAL

Bull seals can grow to over three metres and the cows up to two metres long. They eat fish and are most often seen hauled out on deserted winter beaches and rocks.

WHELK

Points: 5

Whelks move in a similar way to land snails; they creep across the sand and silt on a film of slime. They feed on algae, worms, carrion and other molluscs.

It gets its name from the air-filled bladders which help the fronds of the weed to float.

Points: 10

This type of seaweed is brown and leathery and can grow up to three metres long.

Do you know another name that is commonly given to it?

Points: 10
double with answer

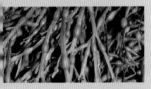

Knotted wracks can live for ten years or more. You can work out its age by counting the large air bladders on a single frond – one for each year of the plant's age.

Points: 10

It gets its name from the toothed edges of the fronds.

Points: 10

SUNSET

Points: 15

At the end of a wonderful day at the seaside, you might be lucky enough to see the sun go down. With the sun disappearing over the horizon and the wonderful colours of the sun, sand and sea, seaside sunsets can be spectacular.

INDEX

i-SPY

How to get your i-SPY certificate and badge

Let us know when you've become a super-spotter with 1000 points and we'll send you a special certificate and badge!

HERE'S
WHAT
TO DO!

✓ Ask an adult to check your score.

✓ Visit www.collins.co.uk/i-SPY to apply for your certificate. If you are under the age of 13 you will need a parent or guardian to do this.

✓ We'll send your certificate via email and you'll receive a brilliant badge through the post!